GREAT PIANO SOLOS

GW00580096

Wise Publications
London/New York/Paris/Sydney/Copenhagen/Madrid

Exclusive Distributors:
Music Sales Limited
14-15 Berners Street,
London W1T 3LJ, UK.

Music Sales Pty Limited
20 Resolution Drive, Caringbah,
NSW 2229, Australia.

Order No. AM970156R
ISBN: 1-84609-390-2
This book © Copyright 2002 by Wise Publications.

Printed in the EU.

Your Guarantee of Quality:
As publishers, we strive to produce every book to the highest commercial
standards. This book has been carefully designed to minimise awkward
page turns and to make playing from it a real pleasure. Particular care has
been given to specifying acid-free, neutral-sized paper made from pulps
which have not been elemental chlorine bleached. This pulp is from farmed
sustainable forests and was produced with special regard for the
environment. Throughout, the printing and binding have been planned to
ensure a sturdy, attractive publication which should give years of
enjoyment. If your copy fails to meet our high standards, please inform us
and we will gladly replace it.

www.musicsales.com

CONTENTS

Ave Maria
(Based on Bach's Prelude No.1 in C Major)

By Charles Gounod

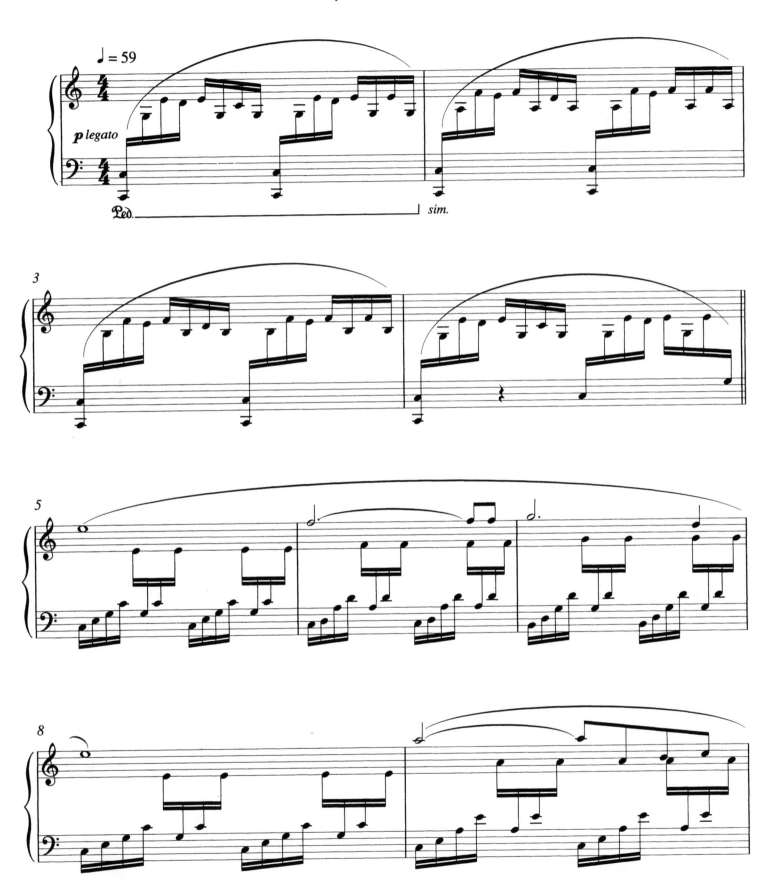

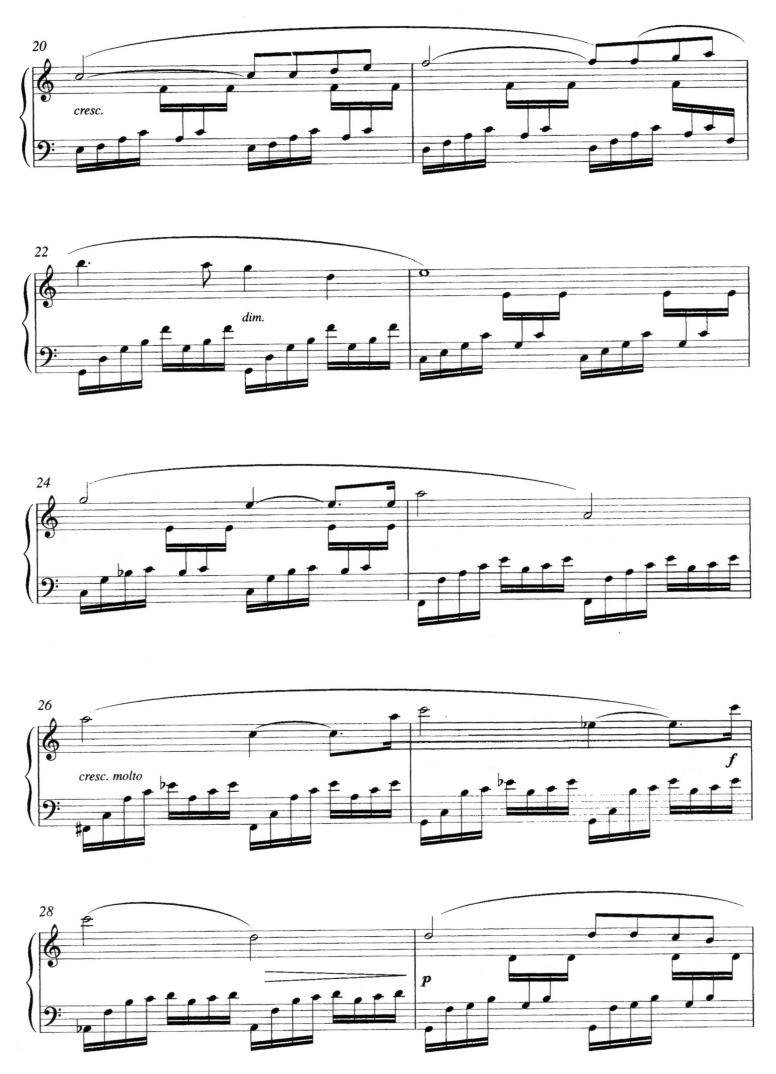

Gymnopédie No.1

By Erik Satie

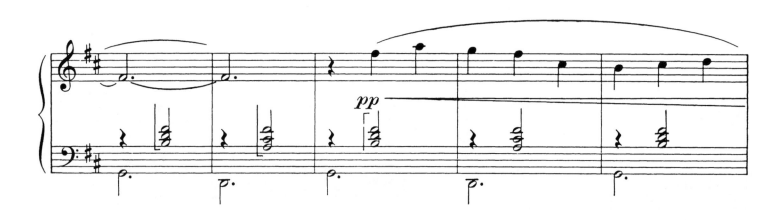

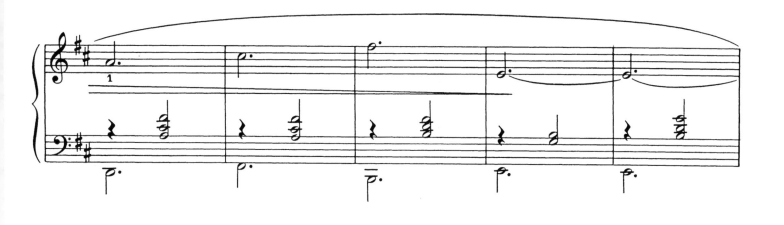

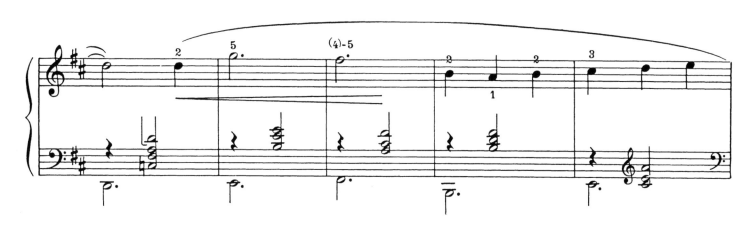

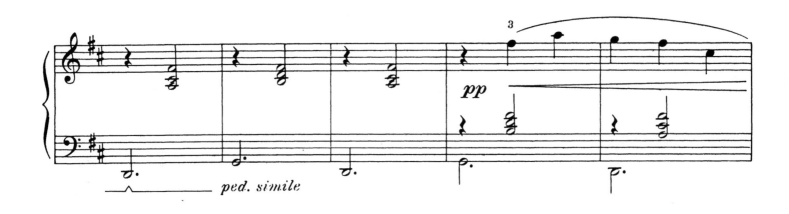

ped. simile

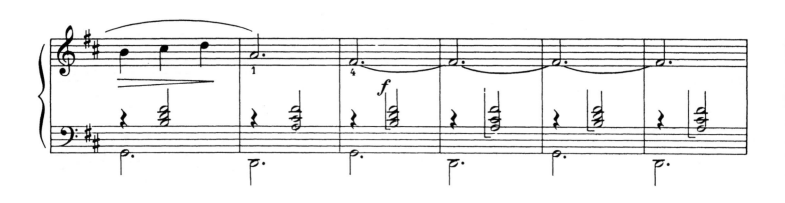

Liebesträume

By Franz Liszt

'Moonlight' Sonata Op.27 No.2
(Adagio sostenuto)

By Ludwig van Beethoven

Adagio sostenuto ♩ = c.50
Si deve suonare tutto questo pezzo delicatissimamente e senza sordini

Adagio from Concerto for Clarinet and Orchestra in A

By Wolfgang Amadeus Mozart

Polovtsian Dances
(from "Prince Igor")

By Alexander Borodin

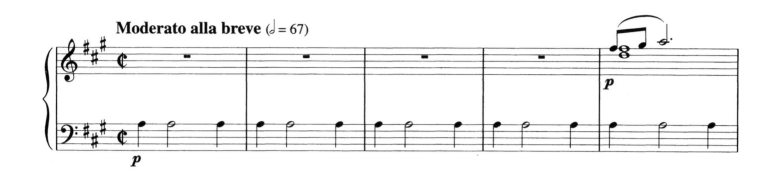

Prelude in D Flat Major No.15 Op.11

By Alexander Scriabin

1) *rit.* }
2) _ _} according to the composer's instructions.

Trumpet Voluntary

By Henry Purcell

Allegro moderato

28

As Time Goes By

(from "Casablanca")

Words & Music by Herman Hupfeld

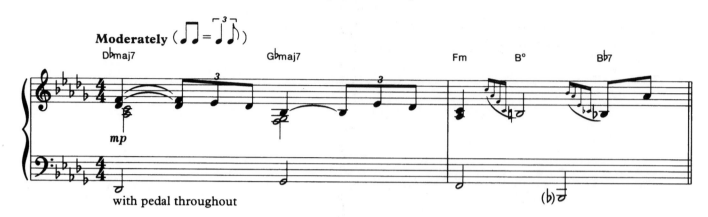

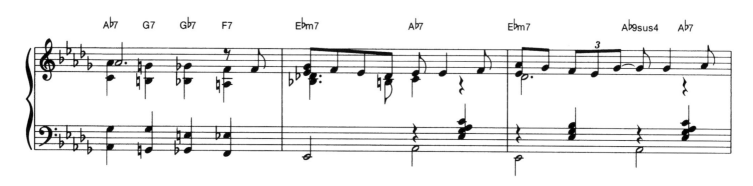

31

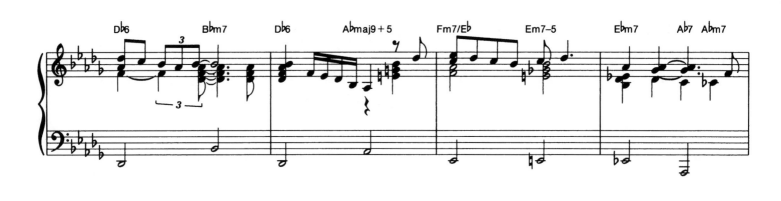

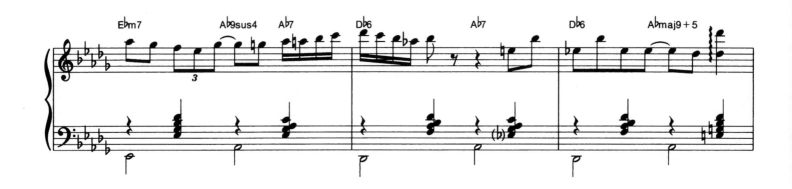

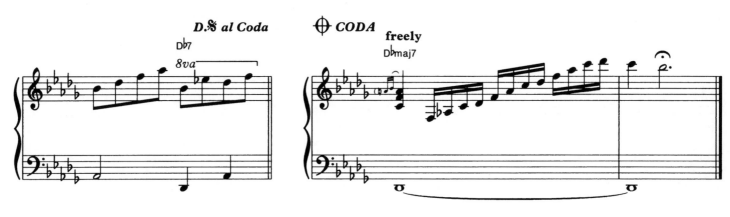

Come What May
(from "Moulin Rouge!")

Words & Music by David Baerwald

The John Dunbar Theme
(from "Dances With Wolves")

By John Barry

D.S. al Coda

CODA

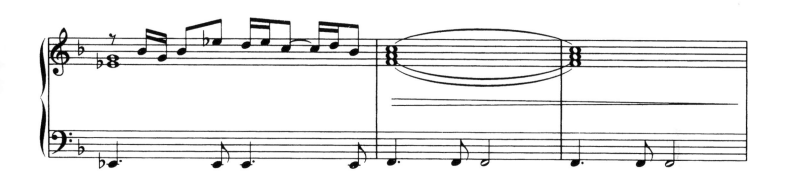

The English Patient / A Retreat / Rupert Bear
(from "The English Patient")

By Gabriel Yared

Plaintively

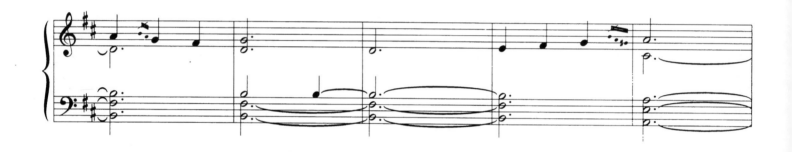

A Retreat

Rupert Bear

The Godfather Waltz
(from "The Godfather")

By Nino Rota

Rubato, expressively

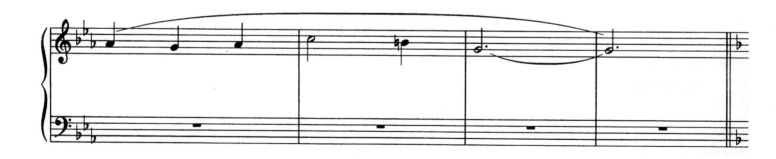

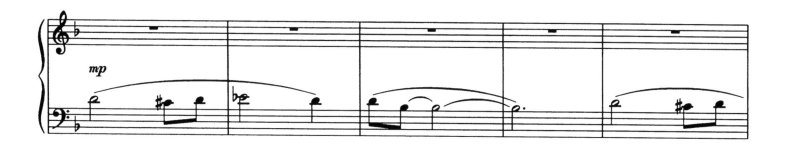

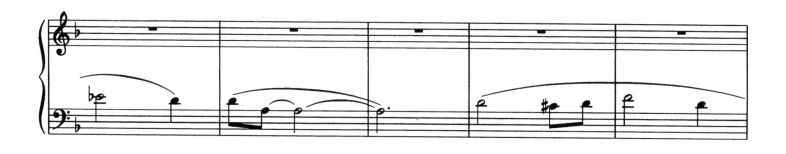

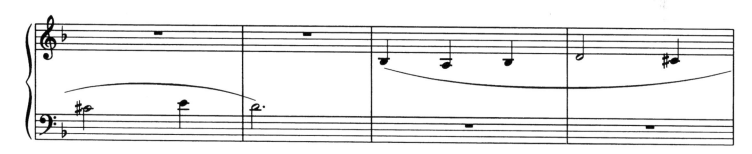

Moderately slow

Jean de Florette
(Theme)

By Jean-Claude Petit

Merry Christmas, Mr. Lawrence

By Ryuichi Sakamoto

52

53

It's A Life
(from "The Truman Show")

By Burkhard Dallwitz

56

All The Things You Are

Words by Oscar Hammerstein II
Music by Jerome Kern

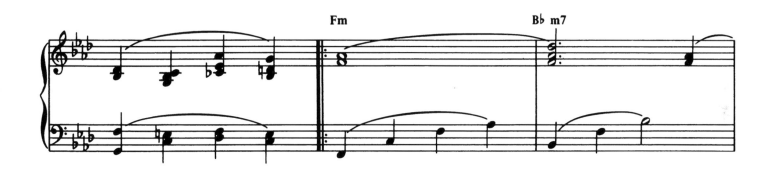

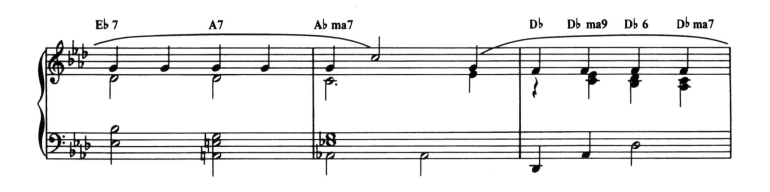

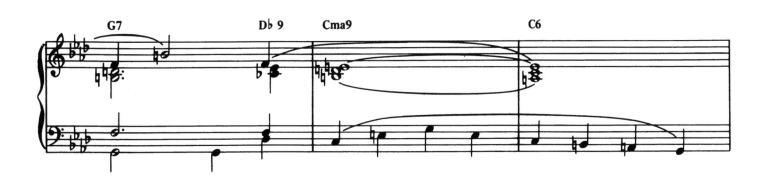

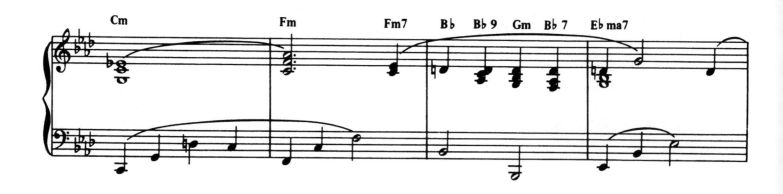

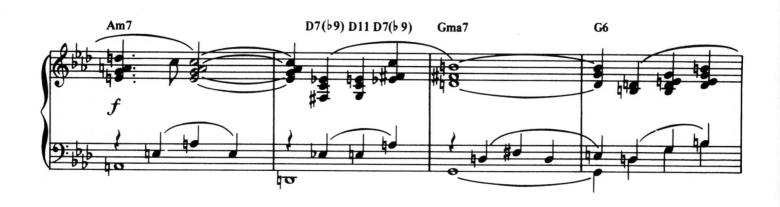

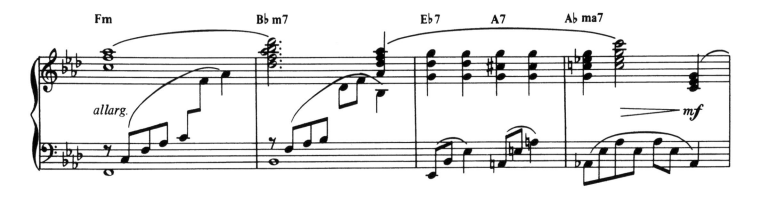

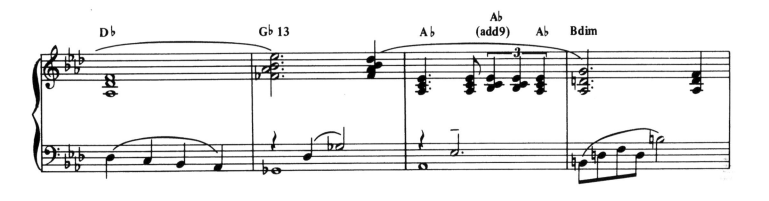

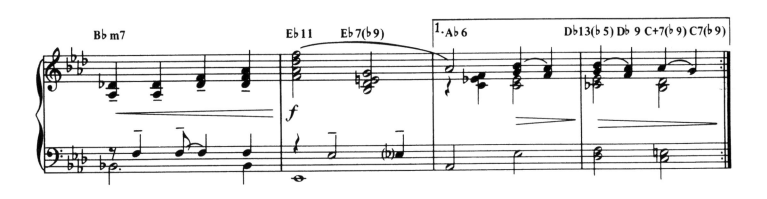

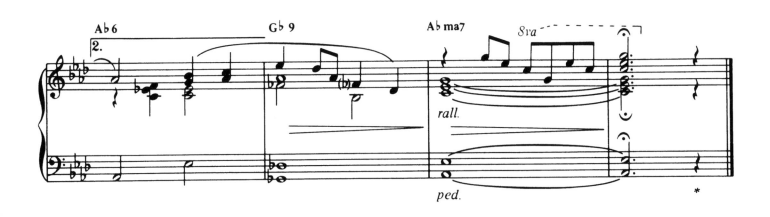

Falling In Love Again

Original Words & Music by Friedrich Hollander
English Words by Samuel Lerner

Tempo di valse andante

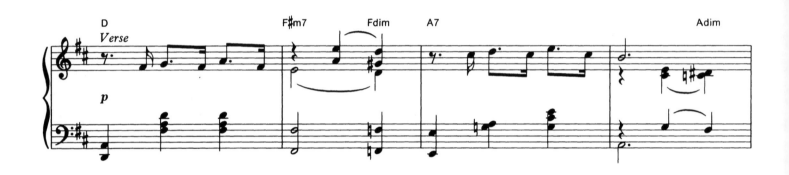

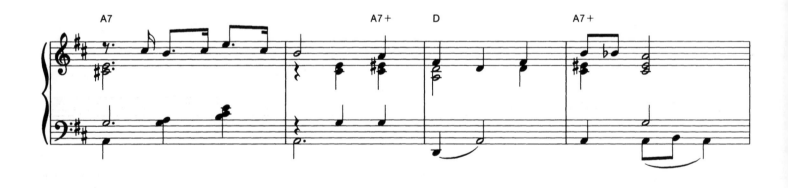

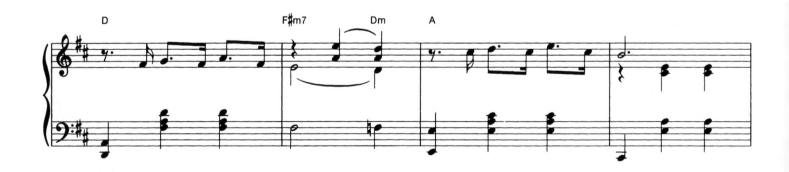

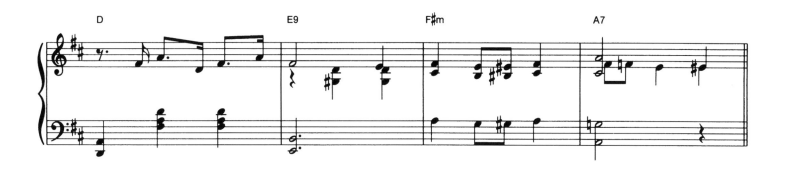

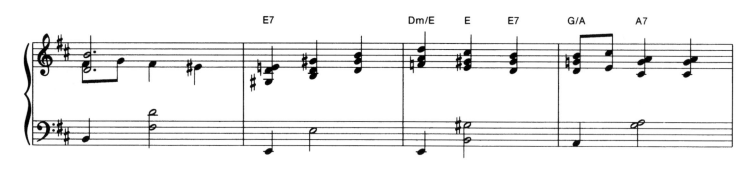

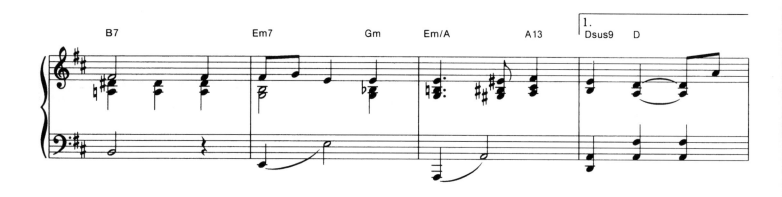

Goldfinger

Words by Leslie Bricusse & Anthony Newley
Music by John Barry

Pennies From Heaven

Words by Johnny Burke
Music by Arthur Johnston

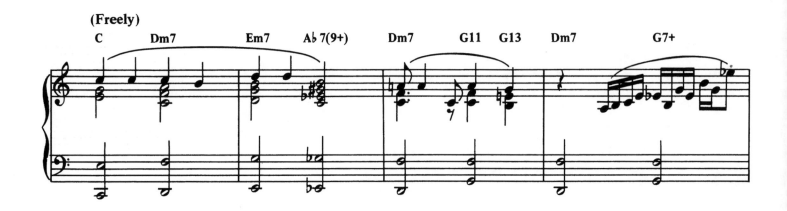

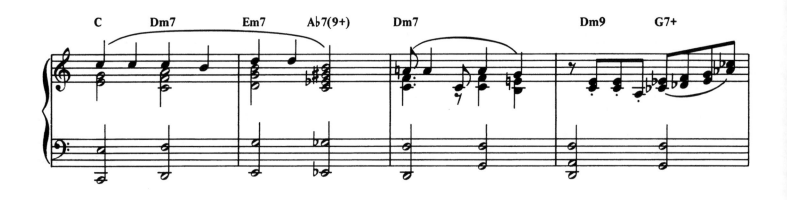

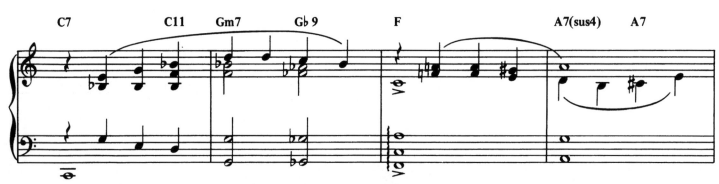

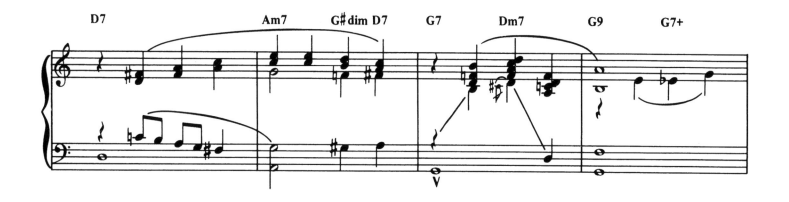

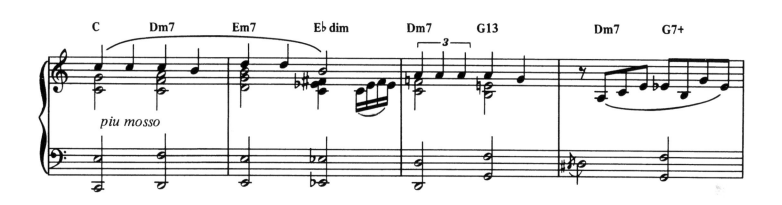

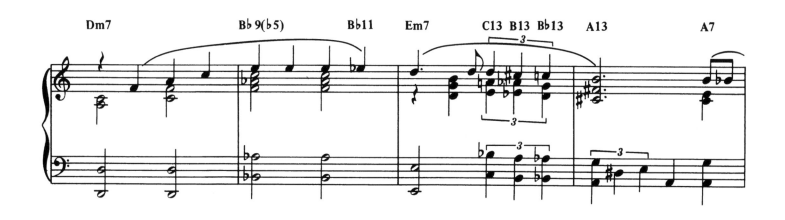

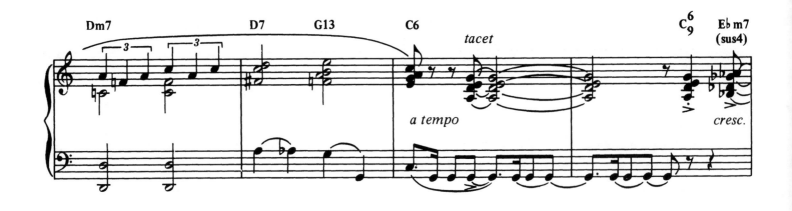

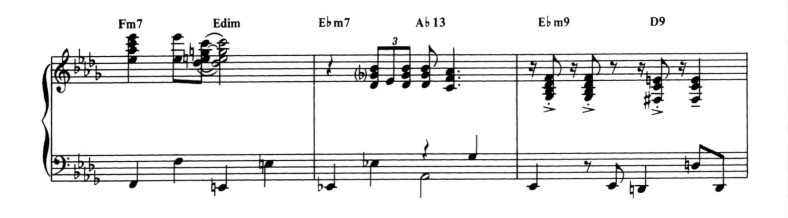

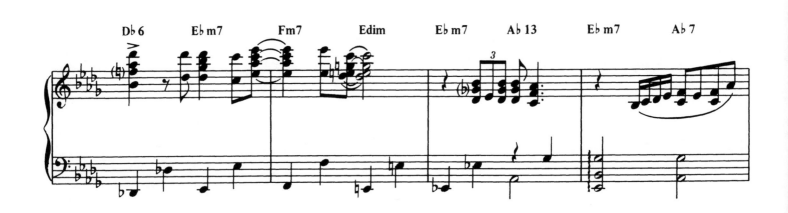

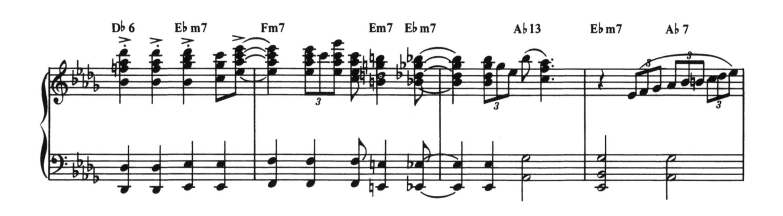

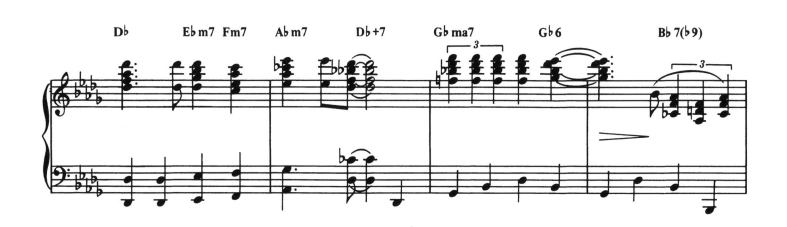

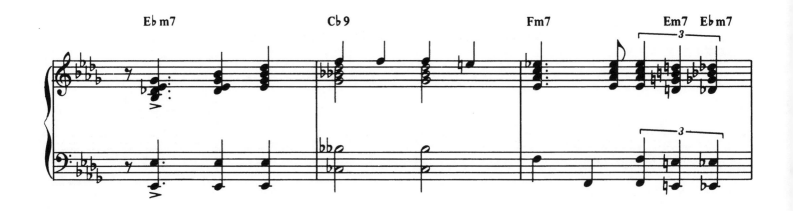

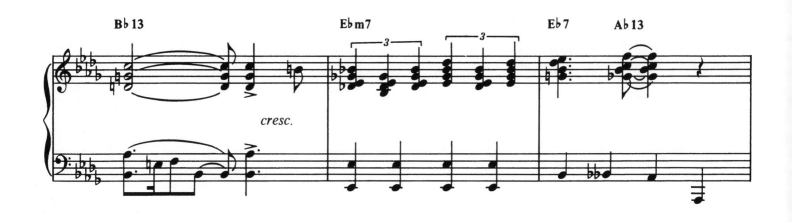

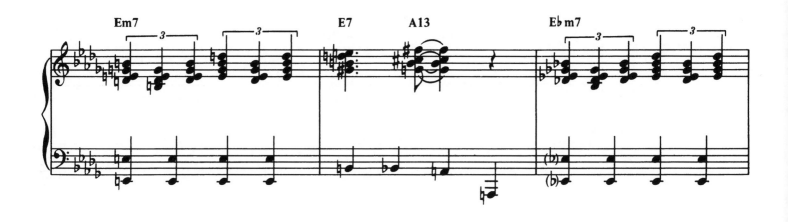

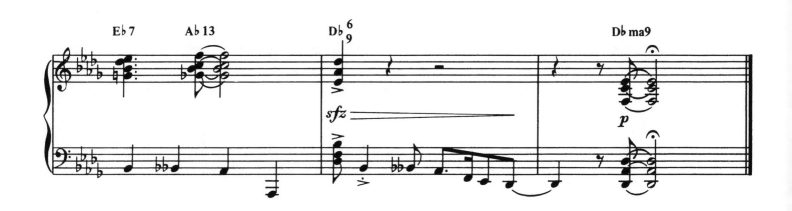

That's Amoré

Words & Music by Jack Brooks & Harry Warren

Moderately bright

Someone To Watch Over Me

Words & Music by George Gershwin & Ira Gershwin

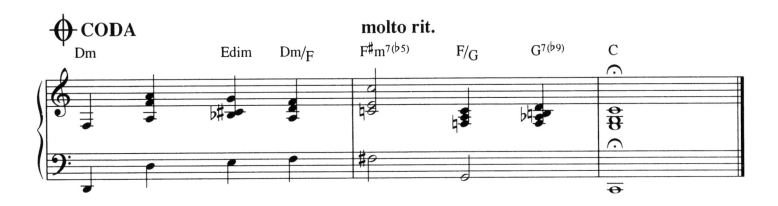

Yesterday

Words & Music by John Lennon & Paul McCartney

What A Wonderful World

Words & Music by George Weiss & Bob Thiele

Bésame Mucho

Original Words & Music by Consuelo Velazquez
English Words by Sunny Skylar

con pedale

To Coda ⊕ **1.**

2.

Cry Me A River

Words & Music by Arthur Hamilton

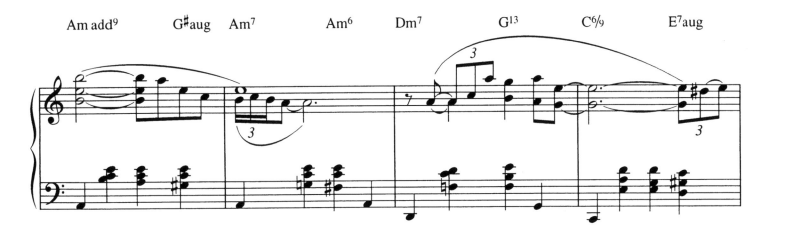

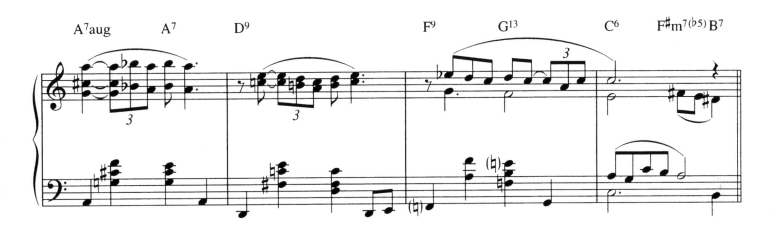

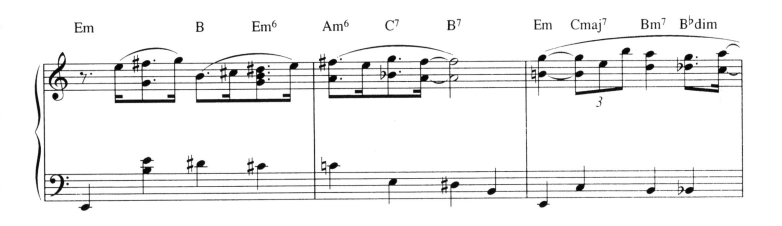

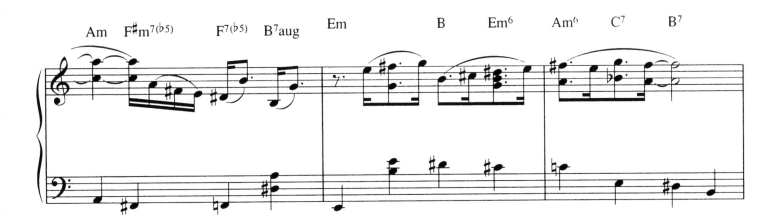

Chelsea Bridge

By Billy Strayhorn

Feeling Good

Words & Music by Leslie Bricusse & Anthony Newley

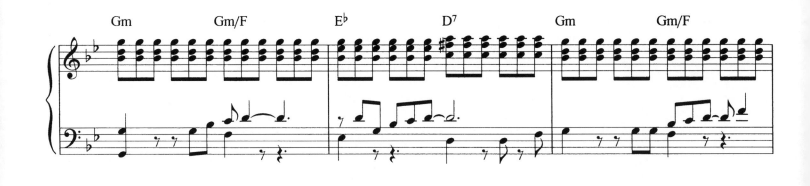

To Coda ⊕

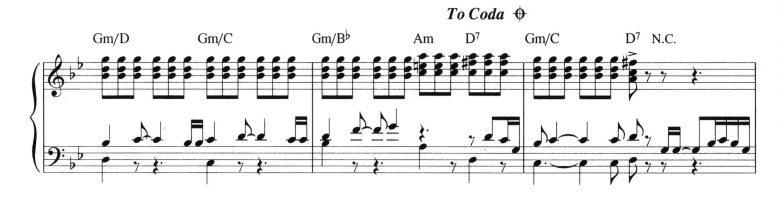

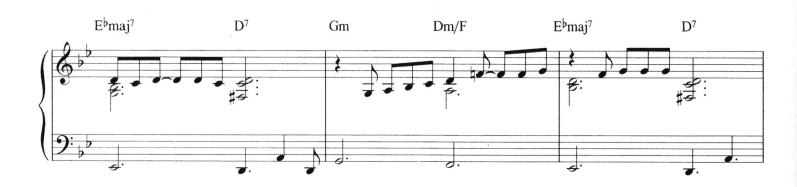

93

In A Sentimental Mood

Words & Music by Duke Ellington, Irving Mills & Manny Kurtz

Need Your Love So Bad

Words & Music by Mertis John Jr.

What'd I Say

Words & Music by Ray Charles

Quiet Nights Of Quiet Stars (Corcovado)

Original Words & Music by Antonio Carlos Jobim
English Words by Gene Lees & Buddy Kaye

Candle In The Wind

Words & Music by Elton John & Bernie Taupin

In a slow 2

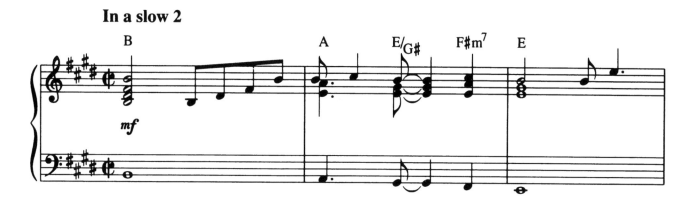

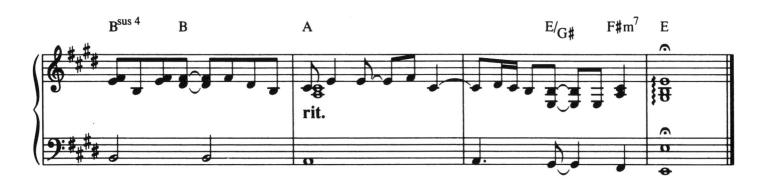

The Air That I Breathe

Words & Music by Albert Hammond & Mike Hazlewood

Angels

Words & Music by Robbie Williams & Guy Chambers

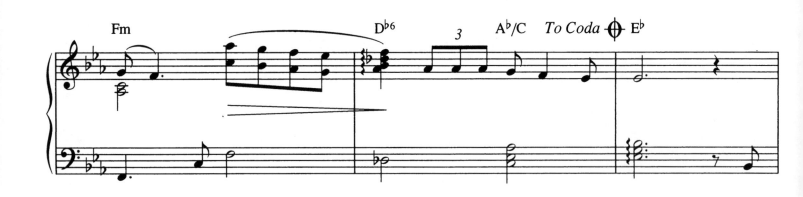

117

(Everything I Do) I Do It For You

Words by Bryan Adams & Robert John Lange
Music by Michael Kamen

Flying Without Wings

Words & Music by Steve Mac & Wayne Hector

I Have A Dream

Words & Music by Benny Andersson & Björn Ulvaeus

126

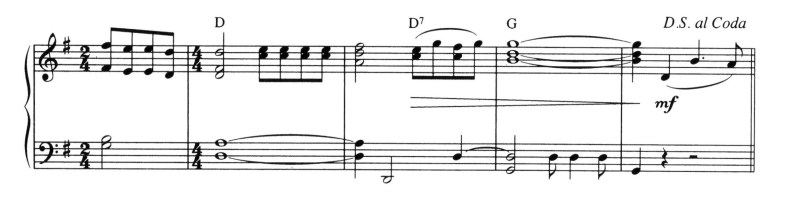

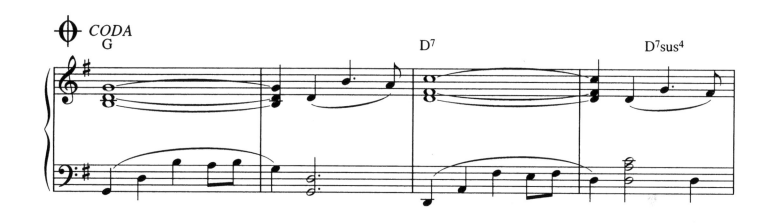

Imagine

Words & Music by John Lennon

129

This Year's Love

Words & Music by David Gray

Cabaret
(from "Cabaret")

Words by Fred Ebb
Music by John Kander

I Whistle A Happy Tune

(from "The King And I")

Words by Oscar Hammerstein II
Music by Richard Rodgers

It Ain't Necessarily So
(from "Porgy And Bess")

Words & Music by George Gershwin, Ira Gershwin, DuBose Heyward & Dorothy Heyward

Luck Be A Lady

(from "Guys And Dolls")

Words & Music by Frank Loesser

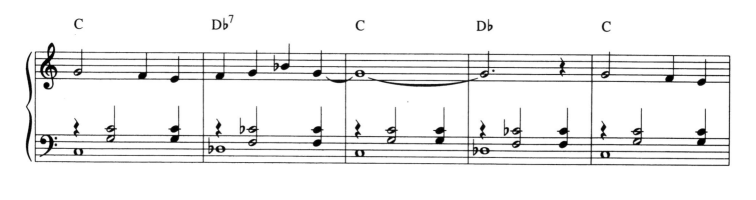

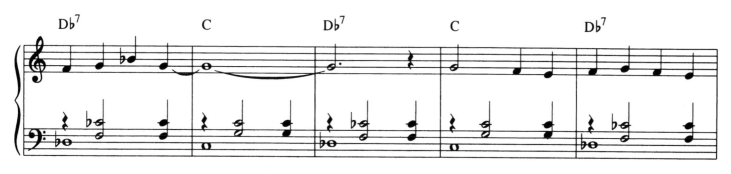

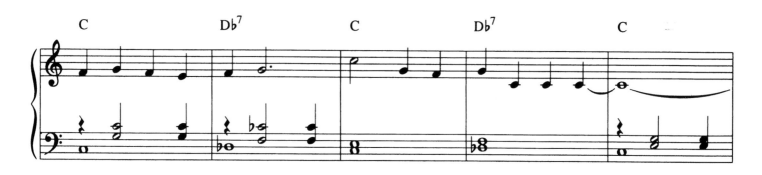

No Matter What

(from "Whistle Down The Wind")

Music by Andrew Lloyd Webber
Words by Jim Steinman

Moderately

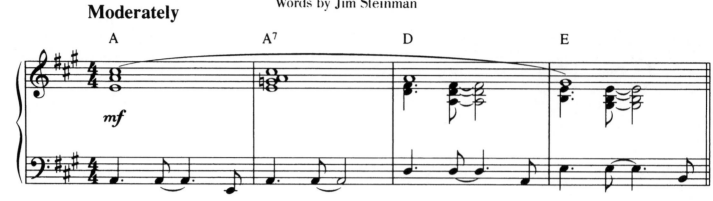

Pick A Pocket Or Two
(from "Oliver!")

Words & Music by Lionel Bart

Till There Was You

(from "The Music Man")

Words & Music by Meredith Willson

153

Wishing You Were Somehow Here Again
(from "The Phantom Of The Opera")

Music by Andrew Lloyd Webber
Lyrics by Charles Hart
Additional Lyrics by Richard Stilgoe

Some Enchanted Evening

(from "South Pacific")

Words by Oscar Hammerstein II
Music by Richard Rodgers